Sam the ram.

Sam is in his pen.

Meg the hen and Sam in the pen.

Sam can run.

Sam the ram can butt.

Sam has fun.

Len the man and Sam in the pen.

Sam can run at Len.

Animal Foods

by Kelly Gaffney

Look at the animals.

The animals are hungry.

Can you see
the blackbird?
It is looking for food.

The blackbird
is eating a worm.

Can you see the big lion?
It is hungry too.

The big lion
is eating meat.

Look at the monkey.

It is hungry.

The monkey
is eating fruit.

Look at the green frog.

It is hungry too.

The green frog
is eating bugs.

Here is a dolphin.
It is hungry.

The dolphin is eating fish.

Can you see the kangaroo?
It is hungry too.

14

The kangaroo is eating grass.

Look at the baby kangaroo.
It is eating grass too.